Lighthouses of Engl

NEEDLES POINT

by

Martin Boyle

and

Ken Trethewey

B & T Publications

Printed by Cedar Press (Southern) Ltd.

PUBLISHED BY B & T PUBLICATIONS,

10 Orchard Way, Highfield, Southampton.

Hampshire SO17 1RD.

International Standard Book Number
ISBN 1-901043-00-2
International Standard Serial Number
ISSN 1363 8009

Printed by Cedar Press (Southern) Ltd.

Lighthouses of Southern England

1. Portland Bill

2. Anvil Point

3. Hurst Point

4. Needles

5. St. Catherine's Point

6. Nab Tower

Hampshire

Southampton

West Sussex

Dorset

Isle of Wight

3 4 5 6

1 2

SPECIAL ACKNOWLEDGEMENT

The authors gratefully acknowledge the invaluable help of the Corporation of Trinity House, its Publications Officer and Media Director, its Director of Engineering and his exceptional Staff, with the full co-operation of the Master and Elder Brethren.

3

NEEDLES POINT

Location: Isle of Wight

Lat/Long: 50.39.07N - 01.35.05W

No. on Admiralty list of lights: 0528

Present lighthouse constructed: 1859

Designer: James Walker

Tower: Granite

Focal plane of light: 27.36 m (89 ft 9 in) above HWST

Light first visible: 22 May 1859

Corporation: Trinity House

Monarch at time of construction: Queen Victoria (1837-1901)

Seafarers approaching the Solent from the west of the Isle of Wight are confronted by the magnificent chalk cliffs above Scratchell's Bay. This part of the Isle of Wight is to the west of Freshwater Bay and gradually rises to a 450 ft (137.16 m) summit at High Down. From here is a view of a lonely lighthouse that stands at the extreme point of a line of chalk soldier rocks known as the Needles. Close to this granite tower lies the treacherous submerged Goose Rock that hides its dangers from the unwary mariner.

Between the fin-like rocks of the Needles is a narrow channel that many 18th century ship masters used as a short cut around the Isle of Wight, a choice regretted on numerous occasions. One such incident brought about a miscarriage of Naval justice and the imprisonment of the wrong man.

As dawn broke on the 25th April 1753, Captain Scorpe handed over command of his warship ASSURANCE to the vessel's 2nd Officer, David Patterson. The only thought on Captain Scorpe's mind was to go to his cabin and prepare for the long awaited reunion with his family at Southampton.

Captain Scorpe had proudly taken command of the 133 ft (40.54 m) long, 44 gun ASSURANCE on the morning of the 29th September 1747, shortly after her launch from the Heather Shipyard at Burlesdon on the River Hamble in Hampshire.

Although an experienced ship master, David Patterson was unsure of the treacherous Needles Channel and made a point of questioning Captain's Scorpe's decision to take this route. But the adamant superior ordered him to continue on the planned course. Even Patterson's comments about the white topped waves near the Needles Channel were ignored by Captain Scorpe who left the bridge and went to his cabin.

Soundings were taken as the ASSURANCE entered the Needles Channel and her passage through seemed clear, until suddenly she struck the submerged Goose Rock. In less than half an hour the ASSURANCE sank and took three of the crew to a watery grave. The remaining survivors, including Captain Scorpe and David Patterson, managed to scramble ashore in Scratchell's Bay.

On the 11th May 1753 a court martial was held in Portsmouth Harbour on board HMS TYGER. The speed with which this judicial hearing was convened was unknown for this period and gives rise to the question that a full investigation had not been carried out. Captain Scorpe gave damning evidence to the naval court that the ASSURANCE was wrecked, not by his hand, but by 2nd Officer Patterson. A senior officer who represented Patterson informed presiding naval officers, including an Admiral, that Captain Scorpe had already been involved with the sinking of another warship in very similar and suspicious circumstances. His remarks were ignored as not being admissible evidence for the case in question.

The court martial lasted less than half an hour before a verdict was reached. The presiding naval officers cleared Captain Scorpe of any blame but found David Patterson guilty under section 26 of the Naval disciplinary code which stated that he had lost one of His Majesty's ships by "unskillful means" upon the rocks. He was sentenced to 3 months imprisonment and his commission taken away. He was ordered to be detained in the notorious Marshalsea Prison in Southwalk, London. This hard labour prison was home to pirates,smugglers and other naval offenders. Once inside the inmates lives were considered unimportant and life expectancy was between 2-3 weeks.

Captain Scorpe was given another commission and later appointed to the Admiralty Board. Nothing further was heard of 2nd Officer David Patterson.

Up to the late 18th century shipping which used the western approaches into the Solent had only the fortifications built by Henry VIII at Hurst Point and Yarmouth, Isle of Wight, as day marks. In 1780 numerous shipowners and Masters petitioned the Elders of Trinity House, for a lighthouse near the Needles Rocks. This application was headed by a wealthy merchant from Ironmonger Lane in London called William Tatnall. He was asked to be a spokesman for a consortium of ship owners who wanted to apply for a Patent to erect a lighthouse on Needles Point.

In January 1781, the Corporation of Trinity House began negotiating with William Tatnall and his consortium but not in respect of a Patent. Instead, the Elder Brethren were strongly opposed to the Needles becoming a privately owned lighthouse. Unknown to William Tatnall, the Corporation had already applied for the Needles Patent and would only consider issuing a lease licence. The terms of the lease prepared by the Elders stated that they wanted three lighthouses built not one. They told William Tatnall that the Corporation was only prepared to issue a licence if the lighthouses for Hurst Point and St. Catherine's were part of the agreement.

Tatnall continued to talk over the proposals with Trinity House and by December 1781 it was agreed that the project would be subject to a survey. At this point in the negotiations the Tatnall consortium would be responsible for building all the lighthouses, all the necessary keepers cottages and roads, to the Corporation's specifications.

The Elder Brethren believed the negotiations would be successfully finalised for the three lighthouses and on this understanding the Corporation obtained their Patent for Hurst Point, Needles Head and St. Catherine's in January 1782. The wording of their Patent read that these lights should be, "kept burning in the Night Season where seafaring men and mariners may take note of and avoid the dangers". It also authorised the Corporation to levy compulsory dues from shipping for their upkeep. The rates to be charged were one penny for English ships and two pence for foreign. This was granted for a period of 50 years. The last part of the Patent stated that the lights should be erected so "His Majesty's ships and other vessels of War might cruise safely during the Night Season in the British Channel".

By the summer of 1782, the negotiations had broken down and were only reopened when William Tatnall was offered £960 per year to build and manage the lights. The lease would be for 21 years and if the initial cost of erecting the lighthouses was above the estimated £2000, the Corporation agreed to increase the annual amount by 10%. All profits from the shipping levies would remain with the Corporation.

Further talks failed to bring about a successful conclusion to the negotiations, even after the Corporation agreed to build the lighthouses themselves. The Elder Brethren also offered the Tatnall consortium £760 per year just to manage the lights and provide keepers and their salaries, and oil. In 1785 the talks broke down completely. William Tatnall felt it was an insult by the Corporation in which all the risk was being taken by his consortium, with Trinity House keeping the profits. They were also annoyed that the original lease agreement stated that the consortium would be responsible for "damage by fire, storm, gales and the firing of cannons on Hurst Castle". Even though the Corporation reworded the lease where it correctly stated the consortium "would not be" responsible for these events, William Tatnall withdrew his offer.

At this stage in the proceedings Samuel Wyatt, the Corporation's Consultant Engineer and Architect, advised the Elder Brethren to obtain the services of Richard Jupp. This architect had formerly been the Chief Surveyor for the East India Trading Company and was already experienced in lighthouse design and construction.

By 1787 Richard Jupp had supervised the construction of a squat 22 ft (6.7m) high lighthouse and adjoining keepers quarters,on the Needles Headland. But within two years the Corporation was forced to abandon the lighthouse because most of the time it was enclosed in sea-mist or fog.

Much of the late 18th and early 19th century shipping avoided the western approaches to the Solent and took the more easterly route past Portsmouth. Rounding the Isle of Wight, however, took more time and was still dangerous, especially with ships under sail. By the middle of the 19th century the need for a light to complement the Hurst lighthouses became a priority. With the dramatic increase in sea trade, there was also a rise in ship wrecks. In 1853 Trinity House instructed its consultant engineer, James Walker, to prepare the plans, specifications and estimates for erecting a lighthouse on the Needles Rocks near Scratchell's Bay.

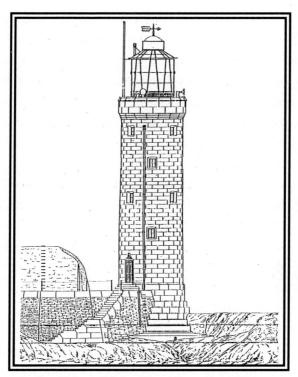

Detail from Trinity House Drawing 45/55.

An application was made to the Lords of the Privy Council of Trade (Board of Trade) by the Elders of Trinity House for the necessary finance from the Mercantile Fund. On the 26th July 1857, James Walker employed local stone masons and quarrymen, to begin the construction of the tower. To supervise the project he appointed Thomas Ormiston resident engineer. From Walker's scribbled drawings, James McConnochie, a draughtsman for Walker and Burgess in London, prepared all the plans and specifications. His older brother had already proved the expertise of the McConnochie family, by assisting Nicholas Douglass during the construction of the Bishop Rock lighthouse in the Isles of Scilly.

The chalk surface of the Needles Point Rock was excavated by the workforce of Thomas Ormiston in conditions where the men were standing constantly sea water. After 8 weeks of back-breaking work, the 3 ft (914 mm) thick granite foundation stones were set into position to form the 38 ft (11.58 m) diameter base for the tower. This first course of stone was laid 3 ft (914 mm) below the low water spring tide level. Above this, the base tapers in a stepped formation to 24 ft (7.32 m) in diameter and consists of 8 courses of chamfered granite blocks 2 ft (610 mm) thick. Each of these stones was dovetailed to the next one and anchored with gunmetal trednails. A further 3 courses of stones brought this base to a height of 21 ft (6.4 m). Central to this base is the tower's water tank, 7 ft (2.13 m) in diameter and 13 ft 4 ins (4.05 m) deep.

After the first course of the tower wall was set into place, the upper 2 ft (610 mm) of its solid base was filled with concrete. This was surfaced with slate 1.5 ins (38 mm) thick with its top level set at 8 ins (203 mm) above the horizontal joint below the wall stones to provide a barrier which would prevent the ingress of sea water through the walls and into the tower. At this level the tower is 21 ft (6.4 m) in diameter and the walls 3 ft 3 ins (994 mm) thick.

The remaining 39 courses of granite blocks raise the Needles tower a further 52 ft 5 ins (15.99 m) in height, to the underside of the cornice stones. At this level the structure is 20 ft (6.1 m) in diameter and the walls 2 ft 4 ins (701 mm) thick. Its 2 ft 3 ins (688 mm) thick cornice stones support the gallery course, which extends the diameter of the lighthouse to 22 ft (6.71 m). These gallery stones were dressed to 4 ft 7 ins (1.4 m) wide and 1 ft 10 ins (572 mm) thick, with a hollowed walkway. A solid moulded granite parapet wall 1 ft 3 ins (381 mm) thick and 3 ft 4 ins (1.02 m) high, tops the edge of the gallery stones. The floor of the lantern room was constructed with chequered steel plates supported by RSJs and surfaced with slate. Its design formed the edges into a watertight joint on to the gallery stones.

The interior of the Needles lighthouse is divided into five apartments. The ground floor and main entrance was used as the oil room, which is 15 ft (4.5 m) in diameter and 10 ft 10 ins (3.3 m) high. A curved tank capable of holding 2500 gallons (11,140 lts) of oil was constructed in this room. The input filler point for the oil supply was fed under pressure through a non-return valve situated at the end of a 4 in (101 mm) diameter pipe built into the base of the tower. The external oil point was positioned 2 ft (610 mm) above the low water spring tide level.

Above the oil room was the provisions store, 15 ft 3 ins (4.65 m) in diameter and 11 ft (3.35 m) high. The next level contains the dining room, kitchen and living quarters, which are comfortably fitted into an area 15 ft 6 ins (4.72 m) in diameter and 11 ft 3 in (3.43 m) high. Purpose-built banana bunks and wardrobes were fitted in the bedroom area on the next level. Each of these bunks had its own privacy curtain. This room is 15 ft 9 ins (4.8 m) in diameter and 11 ft 3 ins (3.43 m) high. The floor above is the watch room. It is 16 ft (4.88 m) in diameter and 9 ft 8 ins (2.93 m) high and provides access to the lantern room. When on duty the keepers spent the majority of their time in this area.

Apart from the concrete ground floor of the Needles lighthouse, all other floors were constructed from chequered steel plate surfaced with Delabole slate. These sections were supported by reinforced steel joists built into the walls of the tower. The edges of the floors rested on 1.5 in (38 mm) wide rebates carved into the granite walls. Access to each level of the tower is by climbing an open plan geometrical steel staircase.

A heavy stormproof entrance door constructed from gunmetal, was fitted on the ground floor and is 3 ft (914 mm) wide and 7 ft 6ins (2.29 m) high. Each apartment has two gunmetal stormproof windows. Those in the provisions store are 2 ft (610 mm) wide and 3 ft (914 mm) high. The remaining windows in the tower are of similar construction but only 2 ft 9 ins (838 mm) high. This was to retain the strength of the wall construction as it diminished in thickness.

From the rear of the tower to the sheer face of the Needles Rock, a 52 ft (15.85 m) long by 26 ft (7.92 m) wide landing stage was constructed. It was formed out of coarsely dressed granite blocks and infilled by much of the excavated chalk and concrete. Its top surface was set 12 ft 4 ins (3.75 m) above HWST. At this level the face of the Needles Rock was excavated to form two stores and an oil room. These rooms had heavy cast iron doors hung in their openings. Access to the tower from the landing stage was up a small semi-circular flight of

granite steps. To allow the keepers to reach the top of the landing stage during low tide, two flights of step iron were fitted to the face of the granite blocks.

While this work was in progress, the workforce of H. Wilkins and Son, of London arrived to erect the lantern. This triangularly glazed unit stood 23 ft 2 ins (7.06 m) in height to the top of its drum ventilator and was 13 ft 1 in (4 m) in diameter. It consisted of an iron pedestal base 5 ft 4 ins (1.63 m) high, which had ventilators devised by Dr. Michael Faraday. Its glazed section was 11 ft 3 ins (3.43 m) in height and topped by a copper-surfaced conical roof. Above this roof was a drum ventilator 7 ft 7 ins (2.32 m) in diameter and 3 ft 10 ins (1.17 m) in height. This unit was surmounted by a 6ft (1.83 m) high lightning conductor and arrow-shaped weather vane. On completion of this work, Chance Brothers of Birmingham installed their 1st order dioptric lens apparatus and the Fresnel multi-wicked oil burner.

While the Chance Brothers workforce was carrying out its part of the contract, the men from Wilkins and Son installed their clockwork mechanism. Part of this work involved the erection of a 1ft (305 mm) diameter hollow cast iron stanchion between the floor of the watchroom and lantern room. Its purpose was to support the weight of the dioptric apparatus and to contain the drive weight of the clockwork equipment that powered the 3 cwt (152 kg) fog bell. During foggy conditions this bell sounded continuously, but after 6 hours of operation, the heavy drive weight had to be rewound by hand to its starting position.

When the Needles Point light was first lit on the 22nd May 1859, the total cost of the project was nearly £20,000, but within a month Trinity House was receiving complaints that the light was not bright enough. At this time the maximum recorded range was 8-9 nautical miles on a clear night.

In the 1860 report of the Royal Commissioners of Buoys, Beacons and Lights personal observations were made by two of the Commissioners, Captain Ryder and Dr. Gladstone, during their visit on the 25th August 1859. Their remarks read:

'It is of grey granite, almost of the same colour as the chalk rock. It is built on the outermost Needles Rock, which has been cut away so as to make a foundation and a platform; cellar and store houses are also cut out of this rock. The illuminating apparatus is dioptric, and the light red. The colour is produced by surrounding the lamp with a screen of red glass, and by placing red shades outside the lens. In parts a cylindrical reflector is placed on the landward side, and there are clear portions to show a white light.'

How the white light was produced seems difficult to comprehend, especially as the report clearly states that the lamp was surrounded by a red screen. The report continued to explain the difficulties involved with obtaining a suitable light intensity.

'The light has to traverse, 1st, the glass chimney; 2nd, the red screen; 3rd, the lens; 4th, a red shade; 5th, the glass of the lantern. The light is said not to be very bright.'

Following the publication of the report, Dr. Michael Faraday, in his capacity of Scientific Officer for Trinity House, asked James Nicholas Douglass, what he thought might overcome the visibility problems. He suggested the removal of the inner red shade and the introduction of various coloured panels of glass fitted to the lantern. By April 1861 the Needles Point lantern panels were of red, green and unobscured natural white. Wilkins and Son had also been commissioned to supply a new occulting mechanism which would operate from the existing clockwork equipment.

The final arrangement for the light provided a main white beam between 300° to 092°. A red light between 092° and 212° covered the approach to St. Anthony's Rocks and the dangerous Dolphin Bank and Shingles. A small white panel of light between 212° and 217° gave a lead before the green sector light of 217° to 224°, with the latter marking the safe channel past the Hatherwood Rocks. Instead of the dark blanking panels, the sector from 224° to 291° had polished copper plates fitted. A small red sector light was also included between 291° and 300°, which covered the Goose Rock. All of these bearings were true if viewed by shipping from a seaward direction.

The occulting sequence was set at a light for 14 seconds, eclipsed for 2 seconds, light for 2 seconds, eclipsed for 2 seconds, every 20 seconds. When these changes were made the white light had a visible range of 14 nautical miles and the red for 9, with the green showing for approximately 6 miles.

For nearly 35 years the only change to the operation of the Needles light was the installation of a Douglass constant level oil lamp. In 1906 the Corporation's Engineer-in-Chief, Sir Thomas Matthews, introduced an incandescent mantle burner. This type of lamp was adapted from the invention of Arthur Kitson and worked on the principle of paraffin gas. The oil was forced under pressure through a vaporiser and into a retort where it was heated. When a white fuming gas developed it was lit above the silk mantle. This lamp effectively trebled the output normally associated with wicked burners and reduced the oil consumption by nearly a third.

In September 1906 the Needles lighthouse became a Lloyd's signal station. This involved the introduction of a morse transmitter and receiver for information on passing ships.

Prior to the commencement of hostilities during the first World War, the Needles Point lighthouse had its fog bell removed and explosive rockets introduced. At this time the Admiralty used the station as an observation post with the morse transmitter employed to provide advanced warning to the Needles gun-battery about German shipping or U-boats. On numerous occasions during 1914 and 1918 these guns were prepared for action, but only fired twice at the enemy.

The second World War saw the Needles Point lighthouse being used on a regular basis for target practise by the gunners of German aircraft. This problem also occurred at the St. Catherine's lighthouse where, sadly, three keepers were killed during a bombing raid. At the Needles station the keepers used one of their storerooms, which had been carved out of the chalk rocks, as their air raid shelter. On several occasions the lighthouse was strafed by machine-gun fire, which shattered sections of the dioptric apparatus. Numerous panes of glass were broken and twice the station was bombed. Luckily the German bomb-aimers were not very good and all the bombs fell harmlessly into the sea.

The Cave Oil Store. (Photo: Trinity House, 1971).

By the end of the War the lighthouse was in need of repair, although it is fair to say, that the keepers did a remarkable job in maintaining the light for the use of passing Allied shipping. It is also important to acknowledge that at no time was this station supplied with a means of defence.

During the summer of 1946 the Needles Point lighthouse was amongst many other Trinity stations around the coast of England, Wales and the Channel Islands that had to be repaired due to War damage. One of the worst affected stations was the Casquets in the Channel Islands. This damage had been caused by British commandos because this lighthouse complex had been turned into a radio directional station which guided German bombers to their targets. It also had a major radio interception unit that could track the movement of Allied shipping. On several occasions British aircraft bombed the Casquets lighthouse, but still the Germans managed to repair their equipment. British commandos carried out a night raid and destroyed much of the equipment, but yet again the station was operational within four days. The War Office ordered another sortie on the Casquets, only this time the commandos were met by four very scared keepers, who apparently had little or no provisions. With their hands in the air, they walked towards the approaching soldiers, one keeper saying that he felt safer with the enemy than being on the receiving end of British attacks. Sir John Bowen, the Corporation's Engineer-in-chief, was given the responsibility of carrying out the necessary repairs to the Needles lighthouse. It was also decided to modernise the station to electrical operation. One of the first considerations given was to the damaged dioptric apparatus, which Chance Brothers stated could not be repaired economically. The Committee of Elders agreed that the best solution was to install a new 2nd order catadioptric unit in its place.

Work began in May 1946 with the first major change to the operation of the Needles lighthouse. The existing oil room was converted to contain the diesel fuel for the generators. These were sited in the entrance room and consisted of 4 L2 Gardener alternator sets which produced 100 volts of electricity. Along with the installation of the new catadioptric lens apparatus, a reed fog horn was fitted with its electrically powered air compressor and air storage tanks sited in the lantern room. When this horn was in serviceit provided a 5 second blast every 20 seconds. Its horn was located on the Needles gallery, with the bell-mouth kept below the focal plane of the light. The light source for the optics consisted of mercury vapour filament bulbs which provided an intensity of 1.5 kw. In case of emergency, these bulbs were sited on a 2 position lamp changer which contained three 36 watt standby lamps. A bank of batteries located in the service or watchroom provided the power for these standby lights. In case of mains failure, or in the event that the keepers were unable to carry out a repair, the emergency lights would remain operational for up to 72 hours. Most of the modernisation programme at the Needles lighthouse was carried out by Chance Brothers and the electrical company of G.E.C. Ltd. This 100 volt power supply would remain in operation for nearly 50 years.

The Second Order Catadioptric lens apparatus fitted in 1946.

When the electrification programme was completed in October 1951, the recorded intensities for the Needles lighthouse were relatively the same. The white light had an intensity of 35,000 candle power with a visible range of 14 nautical miles. The red light was of the same value and visible distance, but the small sector beam over the Goose Rock had a new ruby screen fitted. The effect of this new screen gave the light an intensity of about 14,000 candle powerand a visible distance of 9 nautical miles. Its green sector had an intensity of 8,000 candle power, with a visible range of nearly 7.5 nautical miles. After the project was analyzed following its completion, it was noted that very few problems had been encountered, but the cost of getting the materials and equipment to the Point was fairly high. The Elder Brethren of Trinity House therefore decided that further investigation into electrifying other rock-based lighthouses was needed.

In 1964 a Committee of Elder Brethren visited the station during their tour of various Trinity House lighthouses. They noticed that the external face of the tower rubbed off like a fine powder. Corrosion experts were called in to chemically treat the outside of the lighthouse. Once this work had been completed the lighthouse was redecorated with its central band and lantern area painted red. While this work was being carried out, the keepers' quarters were modernised and the internal areas of the lighthouse redecorated. Up to this time, painting work was normally done by the keepers.

On the 8th July 1971 the existing reed horn was discontinued and replaced by two Supertyfon fog units. These fog horns were constructed from the designs of a Swedish inventor, H. Rydbery, who devised this type of warning signal around 1920. Their principle idea had a vibrating metal diaphragm operated by a system of valves and differential air pressure. The units fitted at the Needles lighthouse were constructed into vertical columns and sited on the gallery. Their audible range was about 5 nautical miles. In service, the sequence of operation was a 1.5 second blast, 2 seconds silence, 1.5 second blast, followed by a 25 second period of silence, repeated every 30 seconds.

Two Supertyfon fog units mounted on the gallery

During April 1986, plans were drawn up for fitting a helipad on top of the lantern. This work involved the removal of the existing domed ventilator, with a new drum unit positioned in its place. Sections of the lantern roof were cut to form access trap-doors and the iron handrail was taken away. All the materials and equipment for carrying out this work were transported to site by Bond Helicopters Ltd. The design of the helipad frame work was similar to a helical lantern, which maximised the unobstructed light area without affecting the strength of its structure.

Transporting helideck materials from ashore.

The support framework of the helipad consisted of tubular steel stanchions that were erected and bolted into position around the lantern. Its square box-shaped steel framing came in three different sections, the lowest part formed into a 5 tier handrail style, the same height as the pedestal base of the lantern. Above this was erected the helically designed section, with its top portion of a similar arrangement as that at the bottom. On to the stanchions and this steel supporting framework was laid the helipad itself. The overall height of this structure, from the gallery walkway to the top of the decking, was 21 ft (6.4 m). It was also 21 ft (6.4 m) in diameter. The landing platform was 26 ft 3 ins (8 m) in diameter, with a heavy duty tensile safety net 5 ft 6 ins (1.7 m) wide around its perimeter. At the four main points of the compass were positioned horizontal siting bars 6 ft (1.83 m) long, with yellow discs at their ends. Access panels were fitted into the helipad for entry into the lighthouse. Further hatches were formed for the water and diesel refuelling points. The maximum design weight for this helipad 3.5 ton (3.6 tonnes). By the 27th September 1987, the helipad was operational.

Helideck nearing completion.

Prior to the introduction of the Needles helipad, all relief changes and provision deliveries were normally carried out by a Trinity House tender or, on the rare occasion, by a helicopter using a hoist from the landing stage. But many of the relief trips were provided by the long standing family of boatmen.

Four generations of these boatmen, including the present member, Tony Isaac, have given faithful service to the keepers of the Needles lighthouse. Tony Isaac remembers standing on the cliffs above the Point as a small boy of six, watching the tracer bullets from German aircraft as they hit the lighthouse. Although he knows the waters around the Needles Point from years of experience, he never forgets how treacherous it can be.

Automation finally came just before Christmas, 1995. The keepers, Principal Keeper Gerard Douglas-Sherwood, who had been at the station since 1982, David Hindmarch, Assistant Keeper since 1991 and Peter Robson, fellow Assistant Keeper since 1993, left the lighthouse for the last time. Prior to this they had carried out duty periods of 4 weeks on the lighthouse and 4 weeks ashore.

During 1994, these keepers had watched a vessel laying a reinforced mains electric cable across the reef from the Needles Battery. When a visit was made to the Needles lighthouse on the 13th July 1994 by a Committee of Elder Brethren, it was noted that this cable showed above the water at low spring tides. Originally it was understood that the heavy cable would settle itself into the sea-bed, but strong tides at the begining of July had proved this to be incorrect. Concrete blocks now anchor this cable safely in place.

When the automation programme was under way, the original Gardner generators were removed after nearly 50 years faithful service. Their removal was the last time a Trinity lighthouse operated from a 100 volt self generating supply.

Today the Needles lighthouse is attended by Tony Elvens, the area keeper, with only the occasional inspection and maintanance being needed. All of the station's operations are now monitored by the keepers at St. Catherine's lighthouse, further along the coast of the Isle of Wight. But after 136 years this Walker designed lighthouse is still operational and must stand as a monument to its builders. Although the human touch is missing, this lighthouse is just as important today as when it was first established. When considering the battles that the Needles Point lighthouse has encountered, with the forces of nature and wartime attacks, its light has remained faithful to everyone who has passed by upon the sea.

To obtain a free list of 'LIGHTHOUSES OF ENGLAND & WALES' booklets and the details of our 'NO OBLIGATION TO BUY', book club, send a S.A.E. to B&T PUBLICATIONS, 10 Orchard Way, Highfield, Southampton SO17 1RD, UK.

To accompany this collection of 'LIGHTHOUSES OF ENGLAND & WALES', the authors have compiled two publications. The first booklet is titled 'BRITISH PHAROLOGY' and gives an easy to read insight into the Corporation of Trinity House, Private lighthouse owners, Royal letter patents and the services which are provided today. The second publication, 'TO LIGHT THEIR WAY' provides a detailed account of the designers, engineers and the builders of the 'LIGHTHOUSES OF ENGLAND & WALES'. It also explains the various light sources, fuels, reflectors and optical apparatus, lanterns and fog warning systems. More importantly it details those men and women who invented, designed and manufactured these items and much much more. Each of these booklets can be obtained from bookshops or direct from the publishers (Post free in the UK).

Also available from B&T PUBLICATIONS: DataBase of the Lighthouses of Great Britain and Ireland. Full colour Windows (3.11 and 95) software. References and locations for over 350 lighthouses. Details of characteristic, fog signals, lat/long, type of tower, date established, history and sources of information. Enlarged and updated each year. Modify the database to suit your own needs. Comprehensive Search and Help functions. Suitable for PC computers with Windows 3.11 or 95 and VGA screen resolution and above. Requires 2Mb hard disk space and 3.5" floppy disk drive. Not suitable for Apple-MacIntosh computers.

For details of the membership for 'THE LIGHTHOUSE SOCIETY OF GREAT BRITAIN' send a s.a.e. to THE SECRETARY, Gravesend Cottage, Torpoint, Cornwall PL11 2LX, UK. Information is also available on the Internet at **http://www.soton.ac./~kt1/**